Mind-Sharpening
Lateral
Thinking
Puzzles

Edward J. Harshman

Illustrated by Myron Miller

Sterling Publishing Co., Inc. New York

For the puzzles following, inspirations are credited to: "Half Jaundiced," adapted from "Bedside Diagnostic Examination" by Elmer DeGowin and Richard DeGowin, 4th Edition, Macmillan, 1981; "No Place for Women," adapted from the comic strip "They'll Do It Every Time" by Jimmy Hatlo, circa 1970; "Catch the Dollar," based on a stunt described in "Science Puzzlers" by Martin Gardner, Scholastic Book Services, 1964; "Not for Ransom," adapted from "Forgive? Forget It!" by Michael Connor, Paladin Press, 1988; "Not a Worthless Check," adapted from a tactic suggested in "Check It Out!" by Edmund J. Pankau, Contemporary Books, 1992.

Edited by Claire Bazinet

Library of Congress Cataloging-in-Publication Data

Harshman, Edward J.
    Mind-sharpening lateral thinking puzzles / Edward J. Harshman;
illustrated by Myron Miller.
        p.   cm.
    Includes index.
    ISBN 0-8069-9432-0
    1. Puzzles. 2. Lateral thinking. I. Title.
    GV1507.L37H37   1997
    793.73—dc21   96-29530
                                                              CIP

10 9 8 7 6 5 4 3 2

Published by Sterling Publishing Company, Inc.
387 Park Avenue South, New York, N.Y. 10016
© 1997 by Edward J. Harshman
Distributed in Canada by Sterling Publishing
℅ Canadian Manda Group, One Atlantic Avenue, Suite 105
Toronto, Ontario, Canada M6K 3E7
Distributed in Great Britain and Europe by Cassell PLC
Wellington House, 125 Strand, London WC2R 0BB, England
Distributed in Australia by Capricorn Link (Australia) Pty Ltd.
P.O. Box 6651, Baulkham Hills, Business Centre, NSW 2153, Australia
Manufactured in the United States of America

Sterling ISBN 0-8069-9432-0

CONTENTS

PUZZLES

How Can This Be?

Ski Through the Tree

The tracks of two skis were visible in the otherwise virgin snow. They led directly to a tree, then the tracks passed the tree—one on each side of it! How were the tracks made?

Clues: 40/Answer: 81.

The Will

A man died, leaving four grown children. His will left one-fifth of his estate to be divided equally among all law-abiding male offspring, three-fifths of it to be divided equally among all female offspring, and the balance to be divided equally among his grandchildren. His offspring were Pat, Leslie, Terry, and Evelyn. Pat had joined the Navy. Leslie gained local notoriety for getting many women pregnant. Terry got a job in a hospital and married a nurse. Evelyn had been convicted of murder and was in prison. After the estate was settled, Evelyn's son had inherited exactly twice as much as anyone else. Explain.

Clues: 40/Answer: 77.

A Gift to Share

Laura won a prize in a fund-raising raffle. It had been donated by a local business, a women's clothing store. "Great!" she exclaimed happily, on hearing of her win. "I know just the person to share it with!" What was it?

Clues: 40–41/Answer: 77.

Half-Jaundiced

Jaundice is a sign of liver impairment that makes the whites of a person's eyes, and the skin of a Caucasian person, turn yellow. One hospital patient had a jaundiced appearance in one eye, but not the other. Why?

Clues: 41/Answer: 79.

One Way to Liberty

To reach the inside of the head of the Statue of Liberty, which stands in New York Harbor, you climb many flights of stairs. When you have almost reached the head, you climb a spiral staircase. While on that staircase, you can look outward and see the inner walls of the statue in all directions; you cannot see a separate staircase next to the one that you are climbing. You are on a staircase that is too narrow for people to go in both directions. Having reached the top, how do you get down again?

Clues: 41/Answer: 86.

Short Swing

Ned, a Little League baseball player, watched the coach open a large box and take out several baseball bats. "That's a big box," said Ned to the coach. "It has to be," replied the coach, "to hold several bats." "Not really," said Ned. "We have a box at home that holds about a dozen and it's only half that size." Does Ned know what he's talking about?

Clues: 41–42/Answer: 88.

The Switch of Mastery

The family was sitting around, reading and relaxing. "This monster is great! He's master of all he surveys," said little Matthew, looking up from a comic book. "If I flip this switch," replied his mother, "*we* will be master of all *we* survey." How?

Clues: 42/Answer: 86.

Hold Still

A professional photographer set up his camera on a tripod, adjusted the aperture, set the exposure speed, and mounted the flash. Then he had his model pose and focused the camera. "Hold still," he said. "The exposure is for one full second." Why, if a flash was used?

Clues: 42/Answer: 85.

Safe Landing

Vic, a seven-year-old boy, was in the park with his mother. He climbed to the top of a hundred-foot tree. Then his mother called him. "Vic, come here!" she shouted. He jumped from the top of the tree, landed uninjured on the ground, and ran to his unconcerned mother. How did he land without hurting himself?

Clues: 42/Answer: 94.

He's All Wet

A man stood outdoors under an umbrella. It was a large umbrella, large enough to cover him completely; and there was no wind. He was not standing in a pond or other body of water. So why was he thoroughly drenched?

Clues: 43/Answer: 74.

No Sale

A telephone solicitor, trying to sell magazine subscriptions, dialed a number chosen at random from the phone book. Instead of the intended recipient, the solicitor reached the circulation manager for the magazine. The telephone solicitor was dialing carefully and did not want to call the circulation manager, but kept reaching the manager anyway, even after trying the number several times. Explain.

Clues: 43/Answer: 82–83.

Spoken by the Book

After a singularly dull lecture that followed a formal dinner, a man walked up to the lecturer and said, "Strikingly unoriginal. I have a book that has every word of your speech in it, and most people here do, too." The lecturer was enraged and demanded proof. He got it. How?

Clues: 43/Answer: 94.

Rope on Its End

A rope is an object that supposedly can be easily carried, but not be stood on end. Can it be stood on end?

Clues: 44/Answer: 86.

Trials of the Uninvited

John was making lunch when his friend Ron arrived, unexpectedly bringing along his two kids and their nanny. Soon, the men, unconcerned, were sitting in the kitchen eating steak sandwiches, while the kids, unfed, played outside under their nanny's watchful eye. When the hungry kids started to chew on strands of grass, the nanny didn't stop them. Why not?

Clues: 44/Answer: 89.

Daffy Decisions

Strong Enough Already

Willie entered an exercise program, and when he finished it his right arm was more than a hundred times stronger than when he had started. He told his friend Spike, a boxer, about this great improvement and the program. Spike thanked Willie for the information, but he was not interested in taking part in the program. Why not?

Clues: 44/Answer: 89.

Time in Reverse

A man wanted a clock for the wall, the traditional kind with an hour hand and a minute hand; but he wanted its hands to move counterclockwise. Why?

Clues: 45/Answer: 82.

Self-Destruction

One approach to reducing health care costs is to discourage self-destructive behavior. Smoking, driving without seat belts, and certain other activities are identified as needlessly risky; and social pressure has built to make them less and less desirable. One form of self-destructive behavior, however, receives little public attention. It can lead to reconstructive surgery, but people who receive the surgery often do not stop the behavior and need the sur-gery again. Oddly enough, the health care administration establishment itself is biased against having this particular self-destructive behavior identified as such. What is it, and why does the health-administration establishment not want it recognized?

Clues: 45–46/Answer: 81.

No Place for Women

High-heeled shoes, girdles, stockings, and other articles of women's clothing have been attacked as the result of a male-dominated society. What characteristic of some women's clothing boutiques can be similarly attacked?

Clues: 46/Answer: 89.

Tricky Tactics

Rainy Walk

Ima Burred Breyne lived in a suburban development and had two parrots. She enjoyed walking in sunny weather, and her parrots enjoyed sunlight too. But she took them outside only during heavy rain. Why?

Clues: 46/Answer: 85.

Scared Mother

A young mother wheeled her baby, in a carriage, through a park. A man looked at the baby and admired it. "What a lovely baby," he said. "Thank you," she replied, smiling gently. A few minutes later, a woman saw the baby and gushed, "What a beautiful boy! I'd love to take him home with me." The mother screamed, snatched up the baby, and ran. Why?

Clues: 46–47/Answer: 76.

Zelda Was Cured

Zelda, who had a one-month-old baby, was five feet eight inches tall. Although she told her doctor about suffering low-back pain, the doctor simply blamed it on the loose ligaments resulting from childbirth and was not very helpful. When she told her husband about it, he promptly did something that greatly reduced her pain and required neither drugs nor exercise. What did the husband do?

Clues: 47/Answer: 77.

She Cheated

A history teacher gave an essay test. To one question, two students, Sherry and Mary, gave identical answers. Their handwriting gave no clue as to who had copied from whom. Nevertheless, the teacher found Mary guilty of cheating. How?

Clues: 47/Answer: 77.

Mowing the Pool

Helen had an in-ground swimming pool with a narrow deck and small lawn next to her home. The pool and lawn were encircled by tall trees which provided privacy. Every week over the summer months, her son first mowed the lawn; then he pushed the lawn mower around the concrete deck that surrounded the pool, although no grass grew there. Why?

Clues: 47–48/Answer: 82.

The Upside-Down Newspaper

A timid-looking man sat on a bench in a city park. He held a newspaper upside down and was reading intently. Why?

Clues: 48/Answer: 77.

Wet in the Winter

Weird Winnie does her laundry in a coin-operated laundromat near where she lives. During the summer, she uses a washer and a dryer for each load of laundry. But during the winter, she uses only the washer and takes her wet laundry home to dry. Why?

Clues: 49/Answer: 83.

Hot Jewelry

Elsie was planning to go away for about a month. She wrapped her good jewelry in a blanket and put it in her self-cleaning oven. Why?

Clues: 49/Answer: 84.

He Held His Liquor

Randy and Andy were at a table in the back of a bar, each holding a bottle of beer. They finished their beer, and Andy got up and walked over to the bartender. He returned with two full beer bottles, handed one to Randy, and sat down. Again, they drank until their bottles were empty. Again, Andy walked over to the bartender and returned with two full bottles. They repeated this process until they had each finished about ten bottlefuls. Randy was, predictably, drunk. Why was Andy nearly sober?

Clues: 49/Answer: 78.

Picking Good Apples

Cora, Flora, and Nora went for a walk in the woods and encountered a tall apple tree. It had wonderful ripe apples; but someone must have been there just before them, for all of the good apples were too high for them to reach. Some worm-infested apples could be easily picked, and more bad apples lay on the ground. How did the ladies gather some good apples?

Clues: 49–50/Answer: 85.

Tied Up in Knots

You have two ropes, a thick one and a thin one. You want to tie one rope to the other one. If the ropes were the same size, or similar in size, you would be able to use any of several knots to connect them. Their differing bulk is a problem, but fortunately not an insurmountable one. How do you do it?

Clues: 50/Answer: 90.

Tiresome Questions

Two suburban neighbors stood, talking, at the small fence that separated their lots. "How tall is your son now?" asked Marla. "He keeps growing, of course," replied Carla, "and I can't really say; but this morning he stood next to my husband's new truck and was just as tall as its right front tire." "How tall is that?" continued Marla. Carla shook her head. "I don't know. My husband's gone now with the truck, and I can't even tell you what kind it is," replied Carla. Marla wandered around the fence and up Carla's driveway, then asked Carla to lend her something. Soon, both of them knew how tall Carla's son was. How did Marla figure it out?

Clues: 50/Answer: 90.

Catch the Dollar

Hold a dollar bill near one narrow edge, with the other narrow edge pointing down, in your right hand. Put your left hand about six inches below your right hand—thumb and fingers separated—ready to catch the bill when you drop it. Let go of the bill. You can easily catch it with your left hand. If others try to catch the bill, placing a hand six inches below yours, and you drop the dollar, it will likely be missed. Unlike you, a second person needs time to react to your action of having dropped it. How can you drop a dollar so as to make it nearly impossible for someone to catch by using thumb and fingers, a pincer grip, as described above?

Clues: 50–51/Answer: 75.

Recycle the Envelope

Prudence sent a letter to a friend of hers, who lived across the country. The letter asked for the return of the envelope, nothing more. Why did she do this?

Clues: 51/Answer: 84.

Old-Time Digital

"This is a CD player," said an electronics store salesman to an old woman. "It gives excellent sound because the signal is recorded digitally. Each individual tone is specially encoded, so you don't hear any background noise. The music sounds the same as when it was recorded every time it's played." "Is that so!" she exclaimed. "Yes. It's relatively new," he continued. "Until a few years ago, all recordings were analog. They picked up background noise and sounded worse the more they were played. "Nonsense!" she retorted. "If digital recordings are what you say they are, I've been using them since I was a little girl!" Explain.

Clues: 51/Answer: 86.

One Must Eat

Still Hungry

A man and a woman entered a restaurant. They sat down, studied a menu, and ordered several dishes. They were presented with a bill and paid it. Then they left, as hungry as when they entered. Explain.

Clues: 51–52/Answer: 88.

Pleased With Pork

A Jewish man who observed religious dietary restrictions went into a restaurant, sat down, and studied the menu. He noticed that pork was served and was pleased. Why?

Clues: 52/Answer: 80.

Eggsasperated!

Bill and Jill were getting hungry. Deciding to eat, they got out a container of several eggs. "Which of these eggs are hard-boiled?" asked Bill. "I don't see Xs marked on any of them." "I didn't bother doing that," replied Jill. "After all, if an egg spins easily, it is hard-boiled. If it wobbles a little, then it's raw." "That's true, but that doesn't help us now!" Bill said, exasperated. Why?

Clues: 53/Answer: 76.

Safe at Home

Carpeted Laundry Room

A year previously, Marjorie had paid a builder for a luxury apartment that had not yet been built. The builder had promised to finish the shared areas of the apartment building and to give her an apartment that was structurally complete, but not to finish the interior of the apartment itself. The builder had, by this time, fully kept his promise about the apartment; and Marjorie was discussing its interior with an architect. She explained: "I want the laundry room to have deep carpeting." "That's risky," replied the architect. "The washer and dryer are against the wall. Suppose the washer breaks down. The first thing the repairman will do is pull it away from the wall and that would ruin the carpeting, right?" "Not the way I plan it," countered Marjorie. Why not?

Clues: 53/Answer: 74.

Nothing Done

When the plans were finished, Marjorie and the architect engaged a contractor to put the panel in the laundry room wall and to lay the carpeting. Marjorie told the contractor: "I'm on the eighth floor. The elevators don't work yet, and there are no floor numbers on the stairway landings. Be sure that your workers count the floors very carefully, because a workman lost count a month ago and remodeled the wrong apartment by mistake." "Dashed impertinent," replied the contractor. "I'll send round some chaps who are especially good at arithmetic." The contractor did so, and a month later sent a bill for work done. When she received the bill, Marjorie walked up the stairs and found that nothing had been done to her apartment. What had happened?

Clues: 53/Answer: 83.

Wrong Again!

On realizing the cause of the error, the contractor was furious. "In this country, the ground floor is 1, climb one flight to floor 2, and so on!" he shouted to the construction foreman. Soon after, the contractor was hired to remove a wall from another apartment in the same building. "The fifteenth floor," the apartment owner told him; and the owner provided a floor plan with the wall clearly identified. But when the foreman and his crew arrived at the fifteenth floor, they encountered painters who were painting the wall that they had planned to remove. What happened?

Clues: 54/Answer: 93.

Hazard in the Code

Building codes are designed to prevent hazards. What common building code provision, if followed exactly, prevents one hazard but permits another?

Clues: 54/Answer: 80.

Sprayed at the Lawn

Henry had a lawn sprinkler installed and connected to a timer. He wanted the lawn watered daily for half an hour late in the day, but not so late that it would still be spraying when he arrived home from work. For a few weeks, the sprinkler worked perfectly. But one day, after he parked his car in the garage and started walking to his front door, the sprinklers turned on and drenched him. What happened?

Clues: 54/Answer: 88.

Sprayed at the Lawn Again

Henry advanced the sprinkler timer and was happy for a couple of weeks. But then, in the middle of the week, he parked his car and walked across the lawn as before and again was sprayed as the sprinklers turned on. Why?

Clues: 54–55/Answer: 94.

Can't Turn It Off!

Wendy noticed light coming from her bedroom lamp, and she wanted the bedroom dark. She turned the lamp switch off, but light continued to shine. She unplugged the lamp, but it continued to provide light. Explain.

Clues: 55/Answer: 75.

A Shocking Problem

Louie and Lucy were in their basement, working on their household wiring. "We need a twenty-foot extension cord," said Louie. He unwound twenty feet of 2-conductor 16-gauge wire from a spool and cut off the right length. He stripped the insulation from both ends. After handing one end to Lucy, he took a plug and fastened it to his end. Lucy worked on the other end. "Ready?" asked Louie. "Yes," answered Lucy. "Let's plug it in and test it," said Louie, putting the plug into an outlet that was connected to a wall switch. As soon as Louie flipped the wall switch, a circuit breaker tripped. What was wrong?

Clues: 55/Answer: 87.

Fix the Furnace

Chilly Chester had called for someone to fix the forced-air furnace. The outdoor temperature was below freezing, and the indoor temperature was about 60 degrees Fahrenheit. When the repairs were complete, Chester walked over to the wall and turned the thermostat to its highest setting. He did not hear the expected sound of the blower motor or feel the draft of air through the vents. Why did the forced-air system blower not react when Chester turned up the thermostat?

Clues: 55/Answer: 76.

She Kept Her Cool

Alexis wanted to air-condition her large living room. She took measurements of the room's dimensions, then went to a reliable store nearby and asked for an air conditioner with a specific BTU rating. "Unless the temperature exceeds 90 degrees," the salesperson said, indicating his choice, "this machine will cool the room well for you." Alexis knew that daytime temperatures of 90 degrees and higher were possible, but rare. "I'll take that air conditioner," she decided, "and a second air conditioner with half that rating." Why?

Clues: 56/Answer: 90.

Good House, Bad Picture

Three young and energetic men got together and decided to enter the house-painting business. Their first client had a house that needed the usual surface preparation. It also had an antenna on the roof that was connected, by a twin-lead wire that ran down the outside wall and through a hole in a windowsill, indoors. One of the men pointed to a splice in the antenna wire that was bulky and appeared to be covered with loose electrical tape. "We could do a nicer-looking job if we first unfastened that TV line and then reconnected it neatly when we were finished," he suggested to the owner. "Please do," replied the owner, looking at the messy installation. "That wiring does look awful anyway." "We'll do a good job," the owner was promised. The three men removed the wire, painted the house, and did a good, neat job of reinstalling the wire. "Something's wrong," complained the owner. "The house looks beautiful, the TV wire looks fine now, but the reception is poor." What happened?

Clues: 57/Answer: 91.

The Bumpy Street

Homeowners along a block got together and grumbled about poor city services. One of them noted the unrepaired potholes in the neglected street and agitated about getting the city to resurface the street. Most of the other people agreed. One homeowner, however, objected. Why?

Clues: 57/Answer: 74.

Safe from the Fire

Somehow during the night, a fire started in the kitchen. The house had no smoke alarm, and flames quickly spread to the only stairway in the house, making it impassable. Husband, wife, and four children were asleep in the house, in their bedrooms. The wife, a light sleeper, luckily awoke just then and jumped up. Within a minute, everyone was outside. How did everyone get to safety?

Clues: 57/Answer: 87.

Travels

No Help

Two men were hiking in the woods. One of them fell and broke his leg. The other wanted to go get help, but both men knew at once that he could not. Why not?

Clues: 58/Answer: 78.

Lost Again

After the man's leg was fully recovered, he and his wife and son went for another walk in the woods. As the sun went down, they gingerly continued walking. Soon they were walking in darkness. "Now what are we going to do?" demanded his wife. "You know the stars, but with the sky overcast we can't see them." "They predicted clear skies, didn't they?" he retorted. Then their son spoke up, announcing brightly, "I know which way is north!" How?

Clues: 58/Answer: 79.

Two Triangular Journeys

Two explorers set up camp at a different latitude and longitude from each other, but less than a day's journey apart on foot. The first day, one of them traveled one mile south, one mile east, and one mile north and ended where he started. The second day, the other one traveled one mile south, one mile west, and one mile north and also ended where he started. Where were they?

Clues: 58–59/Answer: 91.

There Goes the Sun

Edgar the Explorer set out to explore the distant areas of the Earth. One evening, just after sunset, he set up camp. He looked at his trusty compass, and from it he inferred which ways were north, south, east, and west. But the next day, the sun appeared to rise in the west. He looked at his compass again, and the sun was apparently just above the horizon, in the west. Edgar decided not to go anywhere that day, and he watched the sun travel across the sky and appear to set in the east. He never did figure out what happened. Can you?

Clues: 59/Answer: 90.

You Have to Stop

A road that has a STOP sign usually has it at the side, so that a driver will see it, stop, and proceed when safe. When might a STOP sign be in the center of a road?

Clues: 59/Answer: 93.

Two in the Woods

Two people entered the woods for a walk. Later, two people left it. No one else had been in the woods when the two entered it, and no one entered it while the two were walking. Nevertheless, one of the two people who left the woods was soon on the telephone talking about a third person in the woods. Explain.

Clues: 59–60/Answer: 88.

Miracle Shopper

Dolores was sitting and reading in her living room when she realized she needed groceries. She left the room, went outside, and was soon well on her way to a supermarket about half a mile away. Once there, she bought about twelve pounds of food, brought it home, and put it away in her kitchen. She had broken her leg a month previously, did not drive or get into a car or other conveyance driven by someone else. Explain.

Clues: 60/Answer: 81.

Mystery Gate

Some people approaching a five-star beachfront hotel are surprised to see an imposing iron gate blocking a roadway between it and a nearby residential street. Yet it is easy to drive to the same hotel by another route without encountering any gates or security checkpoints. Why is the gate there?

Clues: 60/Answer: 82.

Towing the Car

Police will predictably tow cars if they are illegally parked, obstructing traffic, improperly registered, or encumbered by unpaid parking tickets or other legal actions. When will police tow away a legally parked car with no fault or offense against it or the owner?

Clues: 60–61/Answer: 91.

The Broken Traffic Light

A traffic light, suspended over a street at an intersection, was held in position by a rigid horizontal bar. During a thunderstorm, the bar was struck by lightning and had broken. Now the traffic light was suspended only by its wires. It still faced the intended direction, but the green light was on top and the red light on the bottom. No other working traffic lights faced in that direction. All other traffic lights were undamaged and no police officer was present. A color-blind driver approached the intersection in moderate traffic. Why was there no accident?

Clues: 61/Answer: 74.

Violence, Crime, and Punishment

Death in the Pool

An expert swimmer dived from a diving board into the deep end of a swimming pool, and promptly died as a result. Why?

Clues: 61/Answer: 74.

Legally Castrated

A doctor castrated a fully grown male patient. The patient did not give informed consent for the surgery, had no testicular or other tumor, and had not been charged with rape or any other sex crime. The surgery was done in the USA. It was completely legal. Why?

Clues: 62/Answer: 75.

Rats!

Nasty Nat went to a vacant lot and set and baited about half a dozen rat traps. The next day, he picked up the traps, each one having caught a rat. Then he carefully broke into a house and put the traps, with rats, in it. He was not motivated by revenge against the owner or occupants of the house. What was he doing?

Clues: 62/Answer: 87.

Unsolved Robbery

Two men were talking. The first man said, "You know that bank robbery two months ago? I understand that the police never caught the robber and don't even have any leads." The other man replied, "So I've heard, but the man who did it will spend the next twenty years in prison." Why, if he was not even arrested for the robbery?

Clues: 62/Answer: 93.

This Burglar Got In

A man in possession of several valuable objects fastened quarter-inch plywood over the windows of his house. He boarded over the back door, and he installed a dead bolt on the front door that could be operated only from inside.

Other than the front and the back doors, there were no other entrances. The house was conventionally designed, complete, and intact; there had been no storm damage or other opening to allow easy access to the house. Yet, in no time, a burglar was in the house. How?

Clues: 62–63/Answer: 90.

Silent Murder

The police went to an apartment building to investigate a murder and found the body on the living room floor, with the murder weapon, a shotgun, nearby. The time of the murder was narrowed down to a three-hour period, and the victim's neighbors were questioned. Both of the people in the adjacent apartment, separated from the victim's living room by only a thin wall, were home at the time of the murder. Separately questioned, they both denied hearing a gunshot. The police were not surprised. Why not?

Clues: 63/Answer: 88.

A Matter of Survival

Mort raised himself up and peered uneasily over the counter at his appliance store. Close to a hundred shots had been fired. Three robbers lay dead on the floor, their revolvers in hand. Mort gratefully rubbed the cool quarter-inch steel plating that he had had fastened to the back of the counter. Holding his rifle nervously, he phoned the police: "I want to report an attempted robbery. Three bandits are here, shot, but two got away." The newspapers quickly covered Mort's heroic thwarting of the attempted robbery, going on to say that the police had no leads to the suspects who escaped. Instead of fearing reprisal, Mort was relieved. Why?

Clues: 63/Answer: 80.

Not for Ransom

A woman walked out of her house one evening and closed and locked the front door behind her. Suddenly, three masked men grabbed her and held her at gunpoint. They made her undress completely, unlocked her front door, threw all her clothes and personal belongings inside, threw her keys onto the roof, blindfolded her, drove her to a deserted and unfamiliar part of town, and released her. Just before releasing her, they gave her some money. It would seem that the men's motive was revenge for something the woman had done. But why, given that they were committing a serious crime and intended to cause the woman great distress, did they give her money?

Clues: 63–64/Answer: 75.

Death of a Hunter

Several men went hunting together. They were all familiar with horror stories about people who were shot because they were mistaken for animals by careless hunters, so they all made it a point to wear bright red. None of the hunters was color-blind. They took their shotguns into a forest and waited patiently. After a while, a shot was fired. Because of it, one of the hunters died. Why?

Clues: 64/Answer: 78.

Poker Assault

Eight men decided to play high-stakes poker together. They liked seven-card stud, and they mixed two decks of cards together. After a few hands were played, one of the men carefully picked up the cards, shuffled them slowly and stiffly, handed them to the player on his right to be cut, and took them back. After he had dealt one card to each of five players, three of the other men jumped up, grabbed him, threw him against a wall, and beat him up. Why did they do that?

Clues: 64/Answer: 85.

Unexplained Theft

The back door of the house had a simple lock, and the burglar had no difficulty opening it. Doing so, however, tripped an alarm. The burglar quickly jumped clear of the house and ran as fast as he could, making a successful escape. At first the homeowners were pleased that their alarm system had apparently averted a theft, but when they investigated it was quickly noticed that small valuables were missing from each of several rooms in the house. Explain.

Clues: 64/Answer: 92.

Work Related

Unusual Office Buildings

Grand Central Station, a large railroad station in New York City, has more than 30 platforms at which trains stop and deliver or take on passengers. Underground tracks leave the station and head approximately northward under the street called Park Avenue. Above ground, for about half a mile north of the railroad station, Park Avenue is lined with tall and prestigious office buildings. Intersections in the area follow a decades-old precedent: they each have only one traffic light. In addition, if you walk along that part of Park Avenue and carefully study the buildings on its west side, you will observe that many buildings there share a characteristic, which can be inferred from this description, which is rare in buildings everywhere else. What is it?

Clues: 65/Answer: 79.

Her Good Message

The office telephone rang. A secretary answered it. "No, he left the office an hour ago," she said to the caller, referring to her boss, who stood beside her. After she hung up and identified the caller, he was angry. "Why didn't you put me on? That was an important client!" he demanded. She answered, and he suddenly ran out the door. Why?

Clues: 65/Answer: 91.

Tea Off

As the boss returned from the meeting, he noticed his secretary at the coffee maker. "Are you making coffee?" he asked? "No," she replied, as clear steaming liquid collected in the pot below. Continuing on into his office, he thought, "Good. Tea would hit the spot for a change." He got out a bag of his favorite tea, filled his cup from the pot, let the bag steep a few moments as usual, then took a large sip in anticipation—and promptly spit out the brew! What was wrong?

Clues: 65/Answer: 86.

He Knew His Materials

A newly hired young man at a building contractor's office was asked to buy a left-handed adjustable wrench, a can of striped paint, and a spool of pipe thread. Most newcomers to the trade would have either dismissed the request as a joke, or tried to find the requested materials and looked foolish. But this young man filled the request perfectly. How?

Clues: 66/Answer: 84.

Defying Gravity

Later, the same young man was painting, using an ordinary brush and paint container. Something startled him. He dropped the brush and it fell on the ceiling, not the floor. Why?

Clues: 66/Answer: 76.

Too Heavy

A shipping clerk needed to send a piece of heavy machinery to a customer and preferred using a trucking firm that was both cheap and dependable. Unfortunately, the trucking company had a 75-pound limit per package. The machinery, packed for shipment, weighed 77 pounds and could not easily be disassembled for two separate packages. How did the clerk resolve the problem?

Clues: 66/Answer: 92.

At the Science Lab

The Universal Solvent

"I've discovered a universal solvent," says a scientist. "What do you mean?" you ask. "Just what I said. Everything it touches dissolves and becomes part of it," replies the scientist. "Nonsense! If it does what you say, what could you possibly keep it in?" you retort. What does he keep it in?

Clues: 67/Answer: 92.

Destructive but Useful

A universal solvent, especially the kind that the scientist discovered, is extremely dangerous. How does he plan to use it?

Clues: 67/Answer: 75.

The Microscope

Why does the scientist, an astronomer, have a microscope in his lab?

Clues: 67/Answer: 81.

Sex, Love, and Romance

Passionate Non-Affair

He was married. So was she. But they were not married to
each other. He undressed and got into bed. So did she. He
reached over and touched flesh. She sighed passionately.
Soon, they were making love. But they were not having an
affair. Explain.

Clues: 68/Answer: 84.

She's Not Afraid

Big Bertha, a professional boxer, was being told about a
blind date that someone had arranged for her: "He's a hand-
some six-footer." Bertha was skeptical. "The last six-footer
I encountered," she replied uneasily, "I killed with one blow.
Not just knocked out. Killed." How?

Clues: 68/Answer: 87.

He Won't Hear from Her

Bertha eventually met the man whom she had heard about.
He proved to be six feet tall and very good-looking. They
went to a nice restaurant and later to a nightclub; they had a
wonderful time. Bertha particularly enjoyed his habit of
looking only at her, especially as they spoke, not letting his
eyes wander to other women. At the end of the evening,
Bertha was surprised to hear him say, "I had a wonderful
time, but I know I'll never hear from you." Bertha, who
liked him very much, was confused and upset. But he was
telling the truth. How did he know?

Clues: 69/Answer: 82

Dancing

Bertha's new friend sent her a brief note inviting her for dinner and dancing, and she accepted. Then she wondered how he could manage to dance if he could not hear music. But he managed easily. How?

Clues: 69/Answer: 75.

The Female Customers

The striptease joint was known for its shapely and erotic female performers. Men were a very enthusiastic audience. The management, intolerant of prostitution, disliked female customers. One evening, two women showed up, spoke to the manager, and were admitted. Why?

Clues: 69/Answer: 76.

Brian Braggart

Brian's Space Story

Brian Braggart, teller of tall tales, described his alleged adventure on the moon of a distant planet. "We put on our space suits, left the spacecraft, and explored the moon's surface. When we walked behind a mountain, we saw some little green moonmen. They greeted us in English, and we quickly made friends. They have well-developed legs, and one of them jumped three hundred feet up while describing lunar gymnastics. Their gravity is only about one tenth of ours. Then the moonman told me that my partner said that he had radio trouble, and I looked at my partner and saw the distress signal. We went back to the spacecraft and repaired his radio transmitter." Assuming that space travel to a distant moon is possible and that intelligent life could be found there, disprove the story.

Clues: 70/Answer: 87.

Brian's Fish Story

"Well, anyway," continued Brian, after his first tale had been proved false, "I later went swimming in a large fresh-water lake. I wore a mask connected by a thirty-foot tube to a float on the water's surface and swam along the bottom of the lake. Suddenly, I saw a shark!" Someone interrupted him, protesting that sharks are only found in saltwater. "As I was saying," Brian continued crossly, "I suddenly saw a big fish. Quickly, I took a deep breath and held it as I swam to the surface and to safety." Disprove.

Clues: 70/Answer: 76.

Brian and the Equator

"Well, so that little adventure was all wet," said Brian after his second story was disproved. "But let me tell you about the time I went to Kenya and climbed a high mountain. I was right on the equator and spent a day there. Sure enough, the sun passed directly overhead. The weather was lovely. I phoned a friend, and he said 'Boy, are you lucky! Winter just began, and already we're under a foot of snow.'" Disprove.

Clues: 70/Answer: 80.

Brian and the Ant

"Can I help it if my friend was exaggerating a little bit?" demanded Brian. "But back to me. On my travels, I went to a museum where they had a giant ant, and it was perfectly preserved. Think of it! An ant that looked exactly like tiny, modern-day ants, but as large as a full-grown human being!" Disprove.

Clues: 71/Answer: 94.

Brian in Japan

"Bah, betrayed by an ant! But here's a place I've been, and I have the slides to prove it!" He commandeered a slide projector and put a slide tray on it. Flicking it on, and the room lights off, he began. Up came the first slide. "This is Tokyo. Note the tall buildings, the busy streets ... " The next slide showed a lovely garden in the center of the city. Other slides showed the surrounding countryside and more city scenes. Brian gave his usual long-winded, but plausible, commentary. Finally, a slide showing a factory provoked a protest. "You've never been to Japan, and I can prove it!" How?

Clues: 71/Answer: 92.

Finance, High and Low

The Investment Scam

A group of investors pooled their money and bought into a high-growth mutual fund. A few months later, one of the investors received a telephone call: "This is Justin Peterson, of the Federal Bureau of Investigation. We believe that the fund in which you invested is a pyramid scam. Please withdraw all of your money at once. Will you ask the other investors to withdraw their money, or shall I?" The investors all sent certified letters asking for their money back, but the fund manager had mysteriously disappeared with the money. "He was seen crossing the border into Mexico," reported Justin a few days later. "We will catch him within a month." But he was never caught. Why not?

Clues: 71/Answer: 79.

Table That Plan

A large for-profit corporation bought a controlling interest in a furniture manufacturer and changed the latter's policies. The furniture manufacturer lost money, but the corporate executives were pleased. Why?

Clues: 72/Answer: 89.

Not a Worthless Check

A man requested a check from someone else and threw it away without even trying to cash it. Why?

Clues: 72/Answer: 88.

Money and Laundering

To determine the cost per load of using laundry detergent in a clothes washer, you first determine the per-load wear and depreciation on the washer, then you add the electric and water expense, add the hot water heating expense if the detergent requires warm or hot water, and finally you add the per-load cost of the detergent itself and of any other laundry additives that you use. Right?

Clues: 72–73/Answer: 81.

The Debt Was Paid

For almost half a year, a wholesale merchant had been trying to collect a debt from a small store. The merchant had written increasingly firm letters, but had received no response. Finally, he had had enough. He stormed into the store and demanded, "You see this invoice? Pay it now, or I'll take you to court!" "Has it come to this?" asked the store owner. "Yes!" roared the wholesaler. The store owner opened his safe, took out an envelope, and handed it to the wholesaler. The envelope was full of cash, exactly paying the debt. "But if you had the money, then why did you make me wait?" asked the puzzled wholesaler. Why indeed?

Clues: 73/Answer: 89.

CLUES

How Can This Be?

Ski Through the Tree

Q: Was the tree tall and rigid, not a knee-high sapling that could be skied over?

A: Yes.

Q: Were there ski-pole prints or footprints near the tree showing that the skier removed one ski, or any lightening of either ski track there?

A: No.

Q: Were both tracks made by one expert skier?

A: Yes.

The Will

Q: Were Pat, Leslie, and Terry all law-abiding?

A: Yes.

Q: Did Evelyn's son have any siblings or cousins?

A: No.

Q: Was Leslie paid for getting the women pregnant?

A: Yes.

A Gift to Share

Q: Were two or more separately chosen prizes wrapped together?

A: No.

Q: Was it an ensemble of jewelry or other such set often

broken up into two or more items and generally considered useful alone?

A: No.

Q: Was half of the prize completely useless to Laura?
A: Yes.

Half-Jaundiced

Q: Diagnosing the cause of jaundice in a particular patient requires special medical skill, but can this particular question be answered without it?

A: Yes.

Q: Could the answer be inferred by examining the patient's eyes?

A: Yes.

Q: When a bright light shines on a normal person's eyes, the pupils constrict equally. Would this patient's pupils do so?
A: No.

One Way to Liberty

Q: Is the direction of travel on the staircase reversed every five minutes or so?

A: No.

Q: Is there a hidden elevator or staircase that is behind a wall and that is regularly used?

A: No.

Q: While climbing the spiral staircase, can you see stairs that are intended for downward travel?

A: Yes.

Short Swing

Q: Can Ned's box really hold at least a dozen bats?
A: Yes.

Q: Does it have a lid that opens and closes?
A: No.

Q: Is it designed to be moved from place to place?
A: No.

The Switch of Mastery

Q: Was the mother telling the truth?
A: Yes.

Q: Were there other buildings within a half mile or so?
A: No.

Q: Was the approximate time of day important?
A: Yes.

Hold Still

Q: Was the flash bright for only a very short time, perhaps a hundredth of a second?
A: Yes.

Q: Did it illuminate the background?
A: No.

Q: Was the background very dimly lit?
A: Yes.

Safe Landing

Q: Did Vic land on ordinary hard ground, not in water or on a trampoline or other cushioning object?
A: Yes.

Q: Did his mother fear for his safety?
A: No.

Q: When he jumped from the top of the tree, did he fall less than a hundred feet?
A: Yes.

He's All Wet

Q: Were other people, who stood nearby or walked past the man with the umbrella, wet?

A: No.

Q: Was it raining?

A: No.

Q: Had the umbrella been altered?

A: Yes.

No Sale

Q: Was there something wrong with the telephone, the telephone wiring, or the number that the solicitor dialed?

A: No.

Q: Was the solution to the problem known to the person whose number was dialed?

A: Yes.

Q: Could the intended recipient of the call have only one telephone number in the household or office?

A: No.

Spoken by the Book

Q: Had the lecturer plagiarized from something widely in print or otherwise well known to the entire audience?

A: No.

Q: Did the book contain material that the lecturer did not use?

A: Yes.

Q: Did the words of the lecture appear in the book in the same order that they were used in the lecture?

A: No.

Rope on Its End

Q: If a piece of rope could be made rigid, then could it be stood on end, perhaps leaning against something?
A: Yes.

Q: Does the rope have a hollow interior, like some sash cords, so that a rigid rod can be threaded into it?
A: No.

Q: Is the solution most easily demonstrated with special equipment or during a particular season?
A: Yes.

Trials of the Uninvited

Q: Was anyone upset at the kids' actions?
A: No.

Q: Did the kids complain?
A: No.

Q: Did they usually eat grass?
A: Yes.

Daffy Decisions

Strong Enough Already

Q: Was Spike rational in not wanting to enter the program?
A: Yes.

Q: Was the program intended for athletes?
A: No.

Q: When Willie finished the program, was his arm stronger than it was six months before he started it?
A: No.

Time in Reverse

Q: Was the clock to be used as a joke or a gag?
A: No.

Q: Was the man's occupation important?
A: Yes.

Q: Was his reason for wanting the counterclockwise clock related to a particular characteristic of where he worked?
A: Yes.

Self-Destruction

Q: Has health care administration traditionally been a woman's job?
A: Yes.

Q: In an office setting, is an ambitious woman under pressure to dress elegantly?
A: Yes.

Q: Does the self-destructive behavior have to do with women's clothing?
A: Yes.

No Place for Women

Q: Is it the attitude of the sales staff or a fault in the store's floor plan (cramped dressing rooms, etc.)?
A: No.

Q: Does it concern the merchandise offered rather than any particular article of clothing?
A: Yes.

Q: Is the placement of the merchandise inconvenient?
A: Yes.

Tricky Tactics

Rainy Walk

Q: Did Ms. Breyne's parrots especially enjoy rain?
A: No.

Q: Were they restrained by a cage or leash when outside?
A: No.

Q: Could they fly?
A: Yes.

Scared Mother

Q: Did anyone display a weapon or otherwise threaten the mother?
A: No.

Q: Did the woman resemble anyone who had previously threatened the mother?
A: No.

Q: Had something very unpleasant happened to the mother and her baby?

A: Yes.

Zelda Was Cured

Q: Did Zelda, like many new mothers, often pick up and hold her baby?

A: Yes.

Q: Was her husband taller than her?

A: Yes.

Q: Did Zelda's husband also like to pick up and hold the baby?

A: Yes.

She Cheated

Q: Other than noting that Sherry and Mary had sat next to each other, had the teacher noted anything suspicious as they took the test?

A: No.

Q: Had the teacher graded other essay tests from those same students?

A: Yes.

Q: Did Sherry have a perfect mastery of English grammar?

A: No.

Mowing the Pool

Q: Was the son trying to lengthen the time spent doing the job, perhaps because he was paid by the hour?

A: No.

Q: Was the mower's engine running while he pushed the mower around the pool?

A: Yes.

Q: Are the trees significant?
A: Yes.

The Upside-Down Newspaper

Q: Was the upside-down newspaper a signal to anyone, perhaps a coded message from one spy to another or an attention-getting mannerism to provoke a friendly conversation from a stranger?

A: No.

Q: The man was reading, but was he reading the newspaper?
A: No.

Q: Did the man know that the newspaper was upside down?
A: No.

Wet in the Winter

Q: Is she reacting to the high cost of electricity over the summer or to having an income that varies with the season?
A: No.

Q: Does she live where the winters are very cold, often below freezing?
A: Yes.

Q: During the winter, does she dry her laundry indoors, on racks, at home?
A: Yes.

Hot Jewelry

Q: Did Elsie value her jewelry?
A: Yes.

Q: Was she trying to hide it from burglars?
A: No.

Q: Was she concerned about another hazard?
A: Yes.

He Held His Liquor

Q: Did Andy drink from his bottle, not pour beer on the floor or into a hidden container?
A: Yes.

Q: Did Andy have an unusual tolerance for alcohol?
A: No.

Q: When Andy went for more drinks, did he order two beers?
A: No.

Picking Good Apples

Q: Did Cora, Flora, and Nora shake or climb the tree?
A: No.

Q: Did they prop a fallen branch against a branch of the tree and shake the branch?

A: No.

Q: Would ripe apples fall from the tree after only a minor disturbance?

A: Yes.

Tied Up in Knots

Q: Do you use a particular kind of knot, such as a sheet bend, known to work if the rope sizes aren't too different?

A: No.

Q: Do you unwind and attach strands of the ropes, or use strong glue, tape, or other fastening material?

A: No.

Q: Is the answer to knot one rope first?

A: Yes.

Tiresome Questions

Q: Did Marla ask for any information about the truck or its tire size?

A: No.

Q: Was the new truck ever driven on an unpaved surface?

A: Yes.

Q: Was Carla's driveway paved?

A: No.

Catch the Dollar

Q: Do you distract him just before dropping the dollar?

A: No.

Q: Do you do something beforehand, perhaps get him to arm wrestle, to get his hand tired or tensed up?

A: No.

Q: Might he catch part, but not all, of the dollar?
A: Yes.

Recycle the Envelope

Q: Did Prudence use an unusual stamp and want it canceled and returned?
A: No.

Q: Is it significant that the letter was sent to a distant part of the country?
A: Yes.

Q: Did she have access to a fancy copier, one that could handle odd sizes and thicknesses of paper, including envelopes?
A: Yes.

Old-Time Digital

Q: Are all digital sound-playing devices powered with electricity?
A: No.

Q: Was the woman thinking of a digital sound device that was common soon after the turn of the century?
A: Yes.

Q: Could the device play music from a full orchestra?
A: No.

One Must Eat

Still Hungry

Q: Were the man and woman accompanied by anyone else?
A: No.

Q: Were they surprised or disappointed at anything that happened in the restaurant?

A: No.

Q: Did they sit at a table in a room with other customers?

A: No.

Pleased With Pork

Q: Would a religiously observant Jew eat pork?

A: No.

Q: Did the restaurant represent itself as kosher?

A: No.

Q: When the man entered the restaurant, did he expect to eat there?

A: No.

Eggsasperated!

Q: Was Jill telling the truth about how to identify hard-boiled eggs?

A: Yes.

Q: Was a flat area available, on which to place an egg?
A: Yes.

Q: Could Bill or Jill have identified a hard-boiled egg, under the specific circumstances, by spinning it?

A: No.

Safe at Home

Carpeted Laundry Room

Q: When a clothes washer breaks down, does a repair person usually need access to the back of it?

A: Yes.

Q: Is there any other reason to expect the washer to be moved often?

A: No.

Q: Did Marjorie have special plans for the room behind the washer?

A: Yes.

Nothing Done

Q: Did the contractor intend to cheat Marjorie?
A: No.

Q: Did the workers count the floors carefully, as promised?
A: Yes.

Q: Did Marjorie's future upstairs neighbor have any immediate plans for finishing or remodeling his apartment?
A: No.

Wrong Again!

Q: Were the painters on the correct floor?
A: Yes.

Q: Had the foreman lost count?
A: No.

Q: Could this incident, with the same cause, have happened at a floor numbered ten or less?
A: No.

Hazard in the Code

Q: Can the second hazard be prevented without violating the code?
A: Yes.

Q: Is the hazard commonly observed in residential areas?
A: Yes.

Q: Is it a hazard to able-bodied adults?
A: No.

Sprayed at the Lawn

Q: Had anyone tampered with the timer?
A: No.

Q: Did the incident happen on a Monday?
A: Yes.

Q: Could it recur, for the same reason, within four months?
A: No.

Sprayed at the Lawn Again

Q: Had anyone reset the timer?
A: No.

Q: Did Henry return from work early?
A: No.

Q: If Henry looked around carefully inside his house, could he have discovered what went wrong?

A: Yes.

Can't Turn It Off!

Q: Was it an ordinary electric lamp, with a simple switch, not three-way or battery-powered lamp?

A: Yes.

Q: Was the light coming from the bulb of the lamp?

A: Yes.

Q: Was the light similar in brilliance to a 60-watt bulb, which Wendy liked to use in that lamp?

A: No.

A Shocking Problem

Q: Did Louie or Lucy, while making connections with the ends of the wire, accidentally connect the two conductors together, perhaps by overlooking a loose strand or two?

A: No.

Q: Did Louie put a polarized plug on the wire, so that the plug could fit into the outlet only one way?

A: No.

Q: Were Louie and Lucy clear on what each was to do?

A: No.

Fix the Furnace

Q: Were the repairs completed properly?

A: Yes.

Q: Was the furnace out of fuel?

A: No.

Q: Did the system tested have more than one thermostat?

A: Yes.

She Kept Her Cool

Q: Were both Alexis and the salesperson knowledgeable, and each correct in their assessments of the air conditioners?

A: Yes.

Q: Did Alexis want a second air conditioner for a different room, or as a spare in case the other one broke?

A: No.

Q: When the weather is uncomfortably hot or humid, are the temperature and humidity usually about the same as they were when the weather was previously hot or humid?

A: No.

Good House, Bad Picture

Q: Did the men unfasten the TV wire at the splice and, later, reconnect it with good and tight connections?

A: Yes.

Q: Was the TV reception poor, such as hissing or snow, or were there signs of a bad connection or a weak signal?

A: No.

Q: Should the men have reinstalled the TV wire in a more sloppy-looking way than they actually did?

A: Yes.

The Bumpy Street

Q: Was the objecting homeowner rational?

A: Yes.

Q: If the homeowner sold his house, then would its buyer probably object too?

A: Yes.

Q: Are motor vehicles driven similarly over a bumpy street and over a smooth street?

A: No.

Safe from the Fire

Q: Did the house have any ladders or fire escapes?

A: No.

Q: Was the house split-level or otherwise built into a hill, so that the upper floor could be left without using the stairway?

A: No.

Q: Was the stairway used?

A: No.

Travels

No Help

Q: Could the other man walk normally, in that he had no leg injury?

A: Yes.

Q: Were his mental status and his sense of direction impaired in any way?

A: No.

Q: If he had walked away and sought help, by trying to follow a well-marked trail for two miles, then would he have been likely to find it?

A: No.

Lost Again

Q: Did any of the three have a compass or see familiar landmarks?

A: No.

Q: Did the son infer the direction by the slope of a hill or the flow of a stream or river?

A: No.

Q: Is it important that there was enough light to permit walking, even at night?

A: Yes.

Two Triangular Journeys

Q: Were the explorers on earth, in a polar region?

A: Yes.

Q: Did either or both of them retrace his steps, in the same direction, while traveling?

A: Yes.

Q: Can their exact starting locations be inferred from the description (do exactly two points exist that match the requirements)?

A: No.

There Goes the Sun

Q: Does the sun ever really rise in the west or set in the east, as seen by a stationary observer on earth?

A: No.

Q: Was Edgar on an iceberg that had turned around during the night?

A: No.

Q: Could this incident happen only during a particular time of year?

A: Yes.

You Have to Stop

Q: Is the sign in the path of motor vehicles and not, for example, on the center island of a divided highway?

A: Yes.

Q: After stopping at the sign and proceeding, would a driver usually expect to encounter an intersection?

A: No.

Q: Is the sign on a well-traveled road, one that carries at least one car per hour during the day?

A: No.

Two in the Woods

Q: Was the person on the telephone telling the truth, not lying or describing an optical illusion or hallucination?

A: Yes.

Q: Were the two people who entered the woods related?

A: Yes.

Q: Did both people who left the woods walk out of it?
A: No.

Miracle Shopper

Q: Did Dolores's broken leg have a cast with a strong (walkable) heel on it?
A: No.

Q: Was the street to the store fairly level and well maintained, with little traffic?
A: Yes.

Q: Did Dolores have to struggle to get up from where she was seated and into something else in order go to the store?
A: No.

Mystery Gate

Q: Is the residential street in a bad part of town, an area from which the hotel management feels compelled to take special security precautions?
A: No.

Q: Is the gate there to protect hotel customers from some danger on that part of the hotel grounds?
A: No.

Q: Are hotel customers, in general, expected to use the gated entrance to the hotel?
A: No.

Towing the Car

Q: Is the answer related, directly or indirectly, to a collision involving the car?
A: No.

Q: Is it that the car is parked on a street and the street suddenly needs emergency repairs?

A: No.

Q: Does the owner give permission for the car to be towed?

A: Yes.

The Broken Traffic Light

Q: Did the color-blind driver see something amiss and correctly infer that the traffic light was upside down, identifying its signals that way?

A: No.

Q: Was traffic moving briskly?

A: Yes.

Q: Might there have been a serious accident if the driver had approached the intersection half a minute earlier?

A: Yes.

Violence, Crime, and Punishment

Death in the Pool

Q: Was the pool properly filled with water for swimming; that is, not frozen?

A: Yes.

Q: Did the swimmer expect that he might be hurt in the dive or intend to die (commit suicide)?

A: No.

Q: Other than water, was the pool empty?

A: No.

Legally Castrated

Q: Is the surgery common?
A: Yes.

Q: Did a person other than the patient request and authorize the surgery for that particular patient?
A: Yes.

Q: Did the doctor have an MD or DO degree?
A: No.

Rats!

Q: Although illegal, was Nat's action rational?
A: Yes.

Q: Could it lead to personal gain?
A: Yes.

Q: Did anyone live in the house?
A: No.

Unsolved Robbery

Q: Did the police have any information about the robbery that could lead to an arrest?
A: No.

Q: Did the second man have information that the police did not?
A: Yes.

Q: Is the location of the conversation important?
A: Yes.

This Burglar Got In

Q: Was the burglar hiding somewhere in the house or basement while the man worked?
A: No.

Q: Did the man open the front door from inside and willingly let the burglar in, perhaps because they were friends?

A: No.

Q: Did the burglar intend to steal the valuable objects and remove them from the house?

A: No.

Silent Murder

Q: Were the neighbors deaf?

A: No.

Q: Was there a silencer on the shotgun at the time of the murder?

A: No.

Q: Could anyone have heard the shotgun's being fired at the time of the murder?

A: No.

A Matter of Survival

Q: Were the three dead men really would-be robbers?

A: Yes.

Q: Is it significant that over a hundred shots had been fired but that the three dead men had revolvers, only capable of six shots before needing reloading?

A: Yes.

Q: Was Mort's report to the police entirely accurate?

A: No.

Not for Ransom

Q: Was the money genuine?

A: Yes.

Q: Could it be easily used for a cab to take her home?

A: No.

Q: Do most violent criminals give money to their victims while committing their crimes?
A: No.

Death of a Hunter

Q: Did another hunter, not of the group, careless about the need to identify what is being shot at, fire the shot?
A: No.

Q: Was the shot fired deliberately?
A: Yes.

Q: Was the shot intended to scare or to hit anyone?
A: No.

Poker Assault

Q: When a dealer picks up face-up cards carefully and shuffles stiffly, is there reason to suspect cheating?
A: Yes.

Q: Is it important that more than one deck of cards was used?
A: Yes.

Q: Were the two decks identical?
A: No.

Unexplained Theft

Q: Did the burglar steal the small objects?
A: Yes.

Q: After tripping the alarm and running away, did the burglar return to steal the objects?
A: No.

Q: Would a careful examination of the house reveal what had happened?
A: Yes.

Work Related

Unusual Office Buildings

Q: Does it have anything to do with not having a traffic light on each corner, unlike most New York City intersections that have traffic lights?
A: No.

Q: Do tall and prestigious buildings have elevators?
A: Yes.

Q: Are the elevators equipped with safety bumpers in case, due to mechanical problems, they descend dangerously fast?
A: Yes.

Her Good Message

Q: Did the secretary act in the boss's best interest?
A: Yes.

Q: Had he forgotten something?
A: Yes.

Q: Would the client have been happy to have reached the boss in his office?
A: No.

Tea Off

Q: Had something happened to the stored tea bags that affected their flavor?
A: No.

Q: Had the secretary removed all the coffee grounds and residue from the coffee maker and cleaned it properly?
A: Yes.

Q: Was it the secretary's intention to heat water for tea?
A: No.

He Knew His Materials

Q: Can a left-handed adjustable wrench be distinguished from an ordinary adjustable wrench?

A: Yes.

Q: If you can dip a paintbrush into a can of paint and drag it along a wall so as to produce two strips of different colors, then do you have striped paint?

A: Yes.

Q: Can pipe thread be mounted on a spool?

A: Yes.

Defying Gravity

Q: Was the man working on a stage or movie set showing a house overturned by a bomb or natural disaster?

A: No.

Q: Was he working on an actual house that had really been similarly damaged?

A: No.

Q: Was he using a brush that was of a size and shape normally used for painting houses?

A: No.

Too Heavy

Q: Did the shipping clerk weigh it for the trucking firm on a rigged scale, so that the firm's staff would believe the machinery was light enough?

A: No.

Q: Did he repack it?

A: Yes.

Q: If the machinery was reweighed on reaching its destination, would it appear heavier than when shipped?

A: Yes.

At the Science Lab

The Universal Solvent

Q: Is the solvent inactive unless its components are mixed together, so the components can be stored separately?
A: No.

Q: Can the solvent be held somehow in a special laboratory area or container?
A: No.

Q: Does the solvent have a conventional structure, made up of atoms and molecules?
A: No.

Destructive but Useful

Q: Is the scientist well-meaning and rational, not intending to threaten or to destroy?
A: Yes.

Q: Can the black hole, if properly handled, perhaps eventually reduce or postpone a threat to the earth?
A: Yes.

Q: Is the threat one that the scientific world, and even laypeople, can foresee now?
A: Yes.

The Microscope

Q: Is the microscope used regularly by the scientist?
A: Yes.

Q: Is anything other than astronomy studied in the lab?
A: No.

Q: When special photographs are taken, do astronomers like to study them in great detail?
A: Yes.

Sex, Love, and Romance

Passionate Non-Affair

Q: Were their actions motivated by love, not, for example, an act on a pornographic movie set?
A: Yes.

Q: Were the actions of both known to their spouses?
A: Yes.

Q: Did they love each other?
A: No.

She's Not Afraid

Q: Was Bertha's killing legal?
A: Yes.

Q: Was it in a boxing ring?
A: No.

Q: Was her victim six feet tall?
A: No.

He Won't Hear from Her

Q: Was Bertha's new friend married, aware of something about to happen, or planning to move far away and so become unusually inaccessible or deliberately hard to reach?

A: No.

Q: Would he like to hear from Bertha?
A: Yes.

Q: Although he was not a "blind" date in the visually impaired sense, did he have another common difficulty?
A: Yes.

Dancing

Q: Did Bertha's friend need to watch the musicians, especially the drummer, to follow the rhythm?
A: No.

Q: Did the music have a strong beat?
A: Yes.

Q: Was the rhythm noticeable in the bass?
A: Yes.

The Female Customers

Q: Were the women psychologists, on-duty police officers, or otherwise interested in observing the men patrons?
A: No.

Q: Did the women consistently turn away the men who approached them?
A: Yes.

Q: Were the women's interests similar to those of the male customers?
A: Yes.

Brian Braggart

Brian's Space Story

Q: Could sufficiently intelligent beings study English from radio and television transmissions?

A: Yes.

Q: Could the moonmen have had access to their metabolic equivalents of food, water, and oxygen?

A: Yes.

Q: On the distant moon, with its limited gravity, can people or other beings talk to each other and rely on ordinary sound waves through an atmosphere?

A: No.

Brian's Fish Story

Q: Is it possible to breathe through a tube and swim deep underwater?

A: Yes.

Q: Can nitrogen intoxication (the "bends") be induced by swimming underwater at a depth of thirty feet?

A: No.

Q: Nevertheless, would Brian have been killed by swimming as he described, even if the big fish was harmless?

A: Yes.

Brian and the Equator

Q: Is there a high mountain in Kenya crossed by the equator?

A: Yes.

Q: Can the sun pass directly overhead on the equator?

A: Yes.

Q: Does the sun pass directly overhead daily on the equator?

A: No.

Brian and the Ant

Q: Are there two different reasons why an ant cannot be as large as a person?
A: Yes.

Q: Do ants breathe air into lungs, like people?
A: No.

Q: If an ant were enlarged to the size of a person, then would its strength/weight change adversely?
A: Yes.

Brian in Japan

Q: Were the slides, including the factory one, taken in Japan?
A: Yes.

Q: Did Brian give himself away with any false statements?
A: No.

Q: Did any of the slides show recognizable readable signs or writing using the English alphabet?
A: No.

Finance, High and Low

The Investment Scam

Q: Was the fund manager really a scam artist, who deliberately defrauded the investors?
A: Yes.

Q: Did anyone help him?
A: Yes.

Q: Did anyone look for him?
A: No.

Table That Plan

Q: Were the corporate executives motivated by charity or altruism and attempting to regulate a company that was causing pollution or other social ills?
A: No.

Q: Were the corporate executives trying to destroy a competitor and become a monopolistic supplier of furniture?
A: No.

Q: Did the corporation profit more in its other businesses, because of its management of the furniture company, than it lost in that company?
A: Yes.

Not a Worthless Check

Q: Was the check good?
A: Yes.

Q: Was the check not cashed because it was originally intended to pay a debt that was later canceled or otherwise settled (for example, merchandise originally paid for with the check was returned)?
A: No.

Q: Did the man expect to get more money by not cashing the check than by cashing it?
A: Yes.

Money and Laundering

Q: Is the list complete?
A: No.

Q: Is the incompleteness of the list related to environmental damage, perhaps related to the burning of gas in a dryer or the release of phosphates from detergent?
A: No.

Q: Is the missing item on the list likely to result in an small expense, or cause an increase in a previously existing expense, at least once per month?

A: No.

The Debt Was Paid

Q: Could the debt have been paid when it first became due?

A: No.

Q: Was there a rational reason that the store owner did not pay the debt as soon as he had enough cash to do so?

A: Yes.

Q: Was the wholesaler the only creditor who had debt-collection trouble?

A: No.

SOLUTIONS

Death in the Pool

He hit his head on an inflatable toy, which broke his neck and caused him to drown.

The Broken Traffic Light

The light that faced the color-blind driver was green, though above the yellow and red lenses. He saw the uppermost light glowing and stopped, enraging drivers behind him but not causing an accident.

He's All Wet

The man was a charity volunteer. He had attached small rubber tubes to the umbrella ribs, pierced the tubes with a needle, and connected the tubes to a water source. Now, stationed at a shopping mall, he was deliberately keeping himself wet, seeking donations for flood victims.

The Bumpy Street

The one homeowner lived on the bumpy street, but on the inside of a curve. His driveway met the street between two shade trees. He wanted drivers passing his driveway to go slowly, obeying the speed limit, so that he could see them in time to prevent accidents when exiting his driveway.

Carpeted Laundry Room

Marjorie wanted the room behind the clothes washer and dryer, a bathroom, to have a wall panel that unscrewed from the bathroom side. The panel could be easily removed to provide access to the back of the laundry appliances. This would make repairs easier because the space would be better lit and less cramped than otherwise.

Destructive but Useful

As the sun ages, it will likely expand, eventually heating the Earth and destroying all life. A black hole that orbits the sun and loops through its outer edge, slowly depriving it of luminous matter, may postpone or prevent that process.

Can't Turn It Off!

Wendy's son, as a practical joke, had painted a burned-out bulb with phosphorescent paint, held it in strong light, and screwed it into his mother's bedroom lamp in place of its ordinary bulb.

Not for Ransom

The woman had led an anti-pornography crusade to close a strip joint and stop the sale of girlie magazines in her neighborhood. The gangsters who controlled those businesses were uninterested in creating a martyr, by injury or murder. They reasoned that the woman would react to her abduction by making a police report and her story would be less credible if it included receiving money from her abductors than if it did not. Too, their connections allowed them easy access to large-denomination currency, discontinued in general use many years before. The five-hundred-dollar bill they gave her, though legal, was unfamiliar to cabdrivers and actually added to her frustration in trying to get home. Finally, they bet that her being seen naked on the street, clutching such a large bill, would appear to be a cheap publicity stunt and make her look ridiculous.

Catch the Dollar

Drop not a paper dollar, but a stack of ten dimes. The question did not require the use of a dollar bill.

Dancing

He could feel the vibrations in the air and in the flooring. They gave him enough of a sense of rhythm to enable him to dance.

Legally Castrated

The doctor was a veterinarian and neutered a cat.

Brian's Fish Story

Thirty feet underwater the pressure is greater than on land. Filling one's lungs with high-pressure air and then holding one's breath while ascending to the surface, which is at ordinary pressure, would make one's lungs burst. By gradually breathing out, one can ascend safely.

Eggsasperated!

Bill and Jill were in a moving train, which would make all the eggs wobble similarly, whether or not they were hard-boiled.

The Female Customers

The women were lesbians, and they enjoyed the show just as heterosexual men did.

Defying Gravity

He had been painting the walls of a miniature house, and had turned it upside down to make the work easier.

Scared Mother

The baby, soon after being born, had been kidnapped and almost given, with a forged birth certificate and adoption papers, to a childless couple who wanted a son. Police intervened and restored the baby to the young mother. Still afraid of losing her baby to the couple, she made it a point to dress the boy in colors that didn't denote his sex.

Fix the Furnace

The furnace was designed to circulate air with its blower motor if, and only if, the air in the furnace was hot. Chester had tested the furnace by adjusting the thermostat that controlled the burner. By turning it back and forth, he turned the burner on and off. But there was a second thermostat in the furnace. The second thermostat turned the blower on and off depending on the temperature in the furnace. The furnace needed a few minutes to heat up. The second thermostat meant that, when the burner first came on because the house was cold, Chester would be spared a frigid blast from the still-cold furnace.

Zelda Was Cured

Her husband lengthened the legs of the crib so that the baby could be picked up more easily, without its parents bending so low. The constant bending, especially when the back and pelvic ligaments have become loosened for childbirth, strains the back muscles. Raising the height of the crib reduces the need for bending, a detail often ignored by many obstetricians.

A Gift to Share

Laura had earlier lost an arm in an accident, and the prize she won was an expensive pair of leather gloves. She knew a woman with one arm, the opposite arm, who had the same glove size, and she planned to give this friend the glove that she herself could not use.

She Cheated

The teacher recalled from Sherry's earlier essays, and from the current one, that she confused "its" with "it's." The question in dispute, with both answers identical, included a few misuses of "its" and "it's." Mary used those two words correctly in all her other work, so she must have copied Sherry's answer, errors and all.

The Upside-Down Newspaper

The man was a recent immigrant who did not read English, so didn't realize that the paper he was holding was upside down. As he did not want to be recognized as a foreigner, but enjoyed sitting outside in the park, he was reading his native-language book behind the newspaper, hoping that no one would notice.

The Will

Pat, Leslie, and Terry were women. Leslie worked in a fertility clinic and outraged local religious extremists. Terry married a male nurse. Evelyn, the only son, was not law-abiding and inherited nothing. The estate went 1/5 each to Pat, Leslie, and Terry and 2/5 to Evelyn's son.

He Held His Liquor

Andy, after the first beer, ordered one beer and one serving of soda whenever he walked over to the bartender. He had become tired of being accused of unwillingness to drink heavily, and the bartender cooperated by pouring the soda into Andy's empty beer bottle in return for a good tip.

No Help

The other man was blind. He would have got lost if he had left his seeing but injured companion.

Death of a Hunter

The hunter had climbed up a tree in order to see farther. When he fired his shotgun, the recoil threw him off a limb. Off balance and tangled in the gun-sling, he could not break his fall or reorient himself for a better landing, so he was killed when he hit the ground.

Half-Jaundiced

The patient had a glass eye.

The Investment Scam

The fund manager took money from a few investors, got additional money from subsequent investors, and used that money to give the original investors a good return on their investment. These original investors, happy with their big returns, would recruit their friends and make additional large investments themselves. When the fund manager had enough money from investors, he disappeared. To keep investors from catching him, he had a confederate make telephone calls posing as an FBI agent and diverting attention away from his real hiding place in the USA, and from the fact that no real investigation was already underway.

Unusual Office Buildings

Elevators require bumpers, which are tall, underneath their shafts. Because of the numerous railroad tracks that leave Grand Central Station to the north, some of the nearby Park Avenue office buildings have tracks passing under them, leaving no room for elevator bumpers. The bumpers must be at ground level instead. Therefore, many buildings on the west side of Park Avenue and immediately north of Grand Central Station have escalators to the floor immediately above ground level; and from that floor, elevators lead to all higher floors.

Lost Again

The son could make out that the moon was almost, but not quite, full. If you stand facing south, the changes of phase of the moon move from right to left. A half-moon with its straight edge to the left has a luminous area at its right and is waxing. A half-moon with its straight edge to the right has a dark area at its right and is waning. Because the son saw the moon through the light cloud cover and remembered whether it was getting bigger or smaller, he easily located which way was south and inferred which way was north.

A Matter of Survival

Mort, furious at being robbed almost weekly, invited a couple of friends with semi-automatic rifles to stake out his store. Caught by surprise in a crossfire, the robbers were unable to retaliate or escape, and all three were killed. The police investigator in charge looked at the weapons, the patterns of the bullet holes, and the known felons who lay dead, and guessed what had happened. Sympathetic, the investigator winked at Mort and filed a report that corroborated his story, suggesting that they were not going to investigate further. Mort and his friends considered their clean-up action successful.

Pleased With Pork

The man was a marketing expert hired by the restaurant's owners to increase its business. He was pleased to see that the restaurant already offered several pork dishes, for he knew of a planned advertising blitz by pork producers to promote their product, "the other white meat," and expected pork to increase in popularity.

Brian and the Equator

The sun passes directly overhead on the equator only during the equinoxes. Brian's friend noted that winter had just begun; the time was therefore more than two months away from an equinox. The sun would have passed south of directly overhead if Brian's friend was in the northern hemisphere; it would have passed north of overhead if the friend was in the southern hemisphere.

Hazard in the Code

Electrical outlets, if in walls, must be at least a minimum distance above the floor. This provision protects against electric shock when the floor is washed. Actually placing such outlets at that minimum legal height, however, makes them a hazard to young children, who may become entangled in the wires or "inspect" the electrical outlet too closely. Too, such placement makes outlets inaccessible to adults without stooping. Elderly, tall, or handicapped people may need to ask others, even household children, to plug and unplug electrical devices, because they cannot reach the outlet themselves.

The Microscope

Light passed through a suitable prism is separated into its component wavelengths. Starlight can be passed through a prism and its component wavelengths studied in this way. For very precise work, the wavelengths can be photographed with high-resolution film and the film scrutinized under a microscope.

Ski Through the Tree

The expert skier, familiar with parallel skiing (in which the skis are kept parallel at all times), could ski while wearing only one ski. He made the tracks on two different runs, first passing the tree on one side and then passing it on the other.

Miracle Shopper

Dolores had been paraplegic and wheelchair-bound for years. She had broken her leg in a recent unrelated accident, but easily wheeled herself, as usual, to a local supermarket and back, carrying her groceries on her lap.

Money and Laundering

Laundry detergent, because it is strong enough to attack dirt, may weaken dye or fabric. Ignoring wear on clothing when selecting laundry detergents or other additives can accelerate wear and make clothing wear out faster than necessary. Money and clothes-shopping time can be saved by using a detergent that minimizes damage to clothing, even if the per-load cost of detergent seems high.

Self-Destruction

Women sometimes tend to wear tight-fitting or high-heeled shoes that can lead to hammertoes or bunions. Health administrators, many of whom rationally decide to wear visually attractive shoes, notwithstanding the drawbacks, collectively resist having corrective foot surgery be declared an uninsurable expense, as this would put them at personal material risk.

Mowing the Pool

Leaves falling from the trees would land on the pool deck. The draft from the mower was strong enough to push those leaves away from the pool, so that they would not be blown into it. Using the lawn mower as a blower was faster than raking the leaves.

Time in Reverse

The man was a hairdresser and wanted a clock where he could see it and tell time easily, but where his customers could see it and tell time, too. He did not want a small clock on his counter, because counter space was so limited. He was not allowed to mount anything on the large mirror that was in front of his customers. Therefore, he wanted a backwards clock for the rear wall, so that it would appear correct to customers who looked in the mirror. He knew that he could learn to tell time from it after a bit of practice.

Mystery Gate

The gate is there to block access not to the hotel but to an exclusive luxury housing development situated adjacent to the hotel. This unmanned gate, at the rear of the development's property, is opened only by getting prior permission at a 24-hour-guard security checkpoint at the main gate, or by the wireless-remote gate key provided to the development's residents. Because the very rich residents, and their guests, are generally able to afford and make full use of the facilities available at the luxury hotel, the gate is convenient.

He Won't Hear from Her

He was completely deaf, though a skilled lip-reader. Because of his affliction, he could not literally hear from anyone.

No Sale

Irritated at receiving telephone solicitations, one recipient of them decided to retaliate. He used a caller-ID device to identify the name and phone number of incoming calls. If it was a magazine salesperson, instead of answering the phone he quickly dialed the magazine's circulation department, using a second telephone line, and connected the two lines together. Neither the solicitor nor the circulation manager could easily figure out what was happening, and the manager received the full effect of the nuisance calls.

Wet in the Winter

Winnie knows that heated air can be very dry. She fights low humidity by drying laundry, saving the nuisance of a humidifier and also saving a little money.

Nothing Done

The contractor and his staff were from Britain. Unfortunately, the English start counting floors beginning above the ground-floor level. Their "eighth floor" was, by USA usage, i.e., counting the ground floor as 1, the "ninth floor." They had remodeled the wrong apartment, and its absent owner was not alerted to the error.

Passionate Non-Affair

The man and the woman were in separate locations, involved with their spouses and not with each other.

Recycle the Envelope

The United States Postal Service puts a series of vertical lines (a bar code) on the bottom of ordinary-sized first-class envelopes. These lines permit them to be sorted by machine. Prudence knew that putting a bar code for a distant part of the country on an envelope would significantly delay its delivery. When mailing a check from an interest-bearing account, when the date of postmark is considered more important than the date of delivery, the delay permits additional interest to be earned and can be well worth the effort of copying the bar code onto the envelope.

Hot Jewelry

She had a dependable burglar alarm, but lived in a wooden house and feared fire. She knew that the insulation of a self-cleaning oven, designed for keeping heat in, can also keep heat out. The blanket also repelled heat.

He Knew His Materials

He went to a metalworks shop with an ordinary adjustable wrench and noted the right-hand thread of the adjusting screw and of the set screw that held it in place. He had the metalworks shop make a wrench with left-hand thread for those two parts. Then he took an empty paint can and welded a vertical partition in it, so that the halves could be filled with different colors of paint. He fastened two small paintbrushes together so that they could be handled as a unit, and he delivered the double brush with the two-sided can and explained that the brush should be dipped simultaneously into the two halves of the can and then dragged across a surface to paint stripes. Finally, he found a wooden spool and a short piece of threaded pipe so that the inner diameter of the pipe was slightly bigger than the diameter of the spool. He cut an end off the spool, put the piece of pipe on the spool, and glued the end back onto the spool. He now had pipe thread wrapped around the spool.

Picking Good Apples

The bad apples were not good to eat, but they were available and easily thrown. The ladies merely threw the bad apples at the clusters of good apples and knocked plenty of good apples to the ground.

Hold Still

The background was an open field, and the time was late night. The photographer knew that the field was full of animals at night that were not visible during the day, and he used a long exposure time to capture them. He used a flash to highlight his model in the foreground, knowing that light from the flash would not travel far enough to illuminate the field.

Poker Assault

The dealer was cheating. He had picked up the face-up cards in a careful order so that he would get a good hand; he had only pretended to shuffle the deck, and he had bent the bottom card before cutting the deck and handing it to the player on his right, who would probably cut the deck so as to put the bent card back on the bottom. But his arrangement of good cards was not perfect; he also wanted the very top card to be in his hand. The first five cards, therefore, were not from the top of the deck; they may have been from the bottom. Because he dealt from two different decks that had been mixed together, the other players got suspicious when the back of the top card stayed the same and the first five cards dealt did not all have the same back. That discrepancy proved that the dealer was cheating, and the observant players reacted accordingly.

Rainy Walk

Ima did not want her parrots to fly out of her reach, which parrots can do if full-flighted and taken outside. Heavy rain would wet her parrots' wings and make them incapable of flight, and Ima knew that they could be taken out safely under her umbrella. They would stay dry if they remained with her, but they would be forced to flutter to the ground if they left her.

Old-Time Digital

A player piano has the notes and the times at which they are played encoded on a piano roll. By the salesman's definition, it is a digital sound reproduction device. Older player pianos are powered by a vacuum that is generated by large foot pedals. Another digital sound reproduction device is a wind-up music box.

Rope on Its End

Soak the rope in water so that it is thoroughly wet, then hang it outdoors in subfreezing weather or in a walk-in freezer. When the water freezes, the rope will be sufficiently rigid that a piece of it can stand on end. Soft-laid natural-fiber rope will work more effectively than hard-laid or synthetic-fiber rope.

Tea Off

The secretary had been unhappy with the coffee from the machine and had cleaned it out according to the directions that came with the coffee maker. Diluted distilled white vinegar, poured into a coffee maker in place of water, helps remove mineral deposits. After such cleaning of the machine, water must be poured through it one or two times to fully rinse out the vinegar. You will then have a clean coffee maker that will make better coffee than before. She had not finished the process when the boss made his cup of "off" tea.

The Switch of Mastery

Late at night, in a rural area without nearby neighbors or street lights, the mother could turn off the main light switch and effect complete darkness. Then, they would all be master of all they survey because they could not survey, or see, anything.

One Way to Liberty

Two spiral staircases, sharing the same center axis, are wrapped around each other. While climbing, you can look directly overhead and see the bottom of stairs that are used for descending.

She's Not Afraid

The term "six-footer" can mean someone six feet tall or, as Bertha used it, having six feet—like the cockroach that she had swatted.

Brian's Space Story

With sufficient intelligence and very fortuitous evolution, beings could exist that could learn English and communicate by the same radio frequency that Brian allegedly used. The moon's limited gravity could not retain an atmosphere, necessitating radio or other aids to spoken communication. The moonman jumped off of the lunar surface, and Brian heard it speak. Therefore, it was using the radio frequency and Brian's radio worked. But it also heard the partner's statement about radio trouble, so the partner was able to transmit properly. Brian did not receive his partner's signal even though he could receive and his partner could transmit. They were not separated by a mountain or other large object, for he could see his partner as he gave the visual distress signal. There is the contradiction: he did not receive a signal that he had to have received.

A Shocking Problem

Both Louie and Lucy put a plug on their end of the cord; neither attached an outlet. Both plugs in the cord were plugged into separate electrical outlets connected to the same wall switch and, by chance, the plugs were inserted so as to connect the opposite sides of the electric circuit together. This shorted the circuit and tripped the circuit breaker. Louie and Lucy had not clarified first who should install the plug and the outlet.

Rats!

He wanted to buy the house, which was for sale, cheaply. By making it appear rat-infested, Nat hoped to discourage other potential buyers and get the house for a good price.

Safe from the Fire

The bedrooms were on the ground floor, and the kitchen was on the upper floor. It was easy to leave the house without using the stairway.

Short Swing

Ned's parents, to control insects, have a box not for baseball bats but for the flying mammals. A suitably designed box, open at the bottom and permanently mounted, encourages bats to move in.

Not a Worthless Check

The man had a judgment against a resistant debtor and was interested in locating the debtor's bank account. He wrote a fictitious ad for something that was an excellent bargain and very cheap and sent it to the debtor. The debtor filled out the fake order form and sent a check, easily identifying a bank account that could be impounded. Cashing the check without delivering the promised merchandise would have made him liable for mail fraud and would have been redundant if he could merely seize all the money in the account.

Silent Murder

The shotgun was used to club the victim to death, not to fire a shell or bullet. There was no gunshot.

Sprayed at the Lawn

When standard time was replaced by daylight saving time, Henry forgot to advance the timer on the sprinkler. Relative to his daylight-saving work schedule, the sprinkler started an hour later than before. Unfortunately, that was exactly the time he was crossing his lawn.

Two in the Woods

A married couple, the woman several months pregnant, entered the woods. She suddenly went into labor, gave birth, and collapsed of exhaustion. The man took the baby and quickly went to a telephone to call for help.

Still Hungry

The man and the woman were planning their wedding reception, which was to be at that restaurant. They selected the food to be served and paid a deposit.

Trials of the Uninvited

The nanny and kids were goats, and Ron was trying to convince John to buy them from him to keep John's lawn trimmed.

Strong Enough Already

Willie had had a stroke that temporarily paralyzed his arm. Rehabilitative exercises and neurologic recovery helped him regain some, but not all, of his arm strength.

No Place for Women

Tall people, obviously including tall women, can easily reach high racks or shelves out of reach of shorter people. Conversely, short women can more easily reach shelves nearer the floor than can tall women. Common sense would suggest putting tall sizes on higher shelves or racks and petite sizes on lower ones, but stores often do exactly the opposite. Such a practice may cause a tall woman to have to bend sharply forward, presenting a needlessly awkward display, and force a short woman to request hands-on help when seeking clothing in her size that is out of her reach.

Table That Plan

The corporation was a health and disability insurance company. It encouraged its policyholders, especially business clients for their workplaces, to use furniture designed to minimize back strain and other joint trauma. To do so, it needed a source of such furniture that was not too expensive. Therefore, it bought the furniture company and made it build orthopedically sensible furniture and sell it cheaply. It, therefore, ran at a loss but saved more than enough in reduced disability claims to offset that loss.

The Debt Was Paid

The store owner had customers who were slow at paying their bills. Scared by the wholesaler's letters, he realized their potential effectiveness and sent retyped versions to his customers, collecting from them and gathering money to repay his own debt. He wanted to receive as many threatening letters as possible, so that he could collect as effectively as possible from his customers.

There Goes the Sun

Edgar was in a polar region, between the true North or South Pole and its corresponding magnetic pole. If he was on a line connecting the true and magnetic poles, then the compass directions would be exactly backwards. On the vernal and autumnal equinoxes, the sun rises exactly in the east and sets exactly in the west. At no other time of year does the sun rise and set at exactly opposite points on the horizon. Therefore, Edgar was between a true pole and its magnetic pole during an equinox.

This Burglar Got In

The man *was* the burglar. He had stolen the valuable objects and was preparing to defend himself against a police raid.

Tied Up in Knots

Fasten one rope end to itself, making a loop, then pass the other rope through the loop and knot it to itself. Interlocking bowline knots are commonly used to fasten odd-sized ropes together.

She Kept Her Cool

Alexis knew that too much cooling power makes a room cool, but also uncomfortably humid. If two air conditioners reduce the temperatures of similar rooms by the same amount, a low-power air conditioner lowers humidity more effectively than does a high-power air conditioner. But against extreme heat, a high-power air conditioner is needed. Alexis wanted the flexibility of being able to use either a large air conditioner, small air conditioner, or both. She would use the small one during a humid day with a temperature just slightly above comfortable, and turn on both during a hot and dry spell.

Tiresome Questions

Marla could easily see tire tracks that the new truck had made. She hoped to find, and did, that a small pebble had got stuck in a tire tread. The pebble made a mark on the ground at intervals that matched the tire's circumference. Marla borrowed a tape measure and measured the distance between the pebble marks to learn the circumference of the truck tire, then divided it by 3.14 to calculate the boy's height.

Good House, Bad Picture

The TV wire had been twisted when it was first installed. Twin-lead TV wire not only carries a signal from an antenna, but also picks up a signal by acting like an antenna itself. If the wire is twisted, then the signals it picks up are canceled out, for the signal picked up by one part of the wire is offset by the signal picked up in the reverse direction by another part of the wire. The men installed the wire without such twists, and the owner complained of a double image. The new double image was from the signal picked up by the wire itself.

Her Good Message

The boss had a meeting scheduled with the client at the client's office across town and had not arrived. The secretary inferred that the boss would be better off pleading a traffic jam than admitting that he had forgotten about the meeting.

Towing the Car

If the owner, having legally parked the car on a street or in another public place, is disabled by a sudden illness or accident, the police will sometimes tow the car to a safe place. This action protects the owner from damage to the apparently abandoned car and from parking tickets, if the parking space is legal only during certain times of day.

Two Triangular Journeys

At a certain latitude very near the South Pole, traveling east or west for one mile describes a complete circle; the endpoint is the same as the starting point. One of the explorers could have started from any point one mile north of this circle. Slightly south of the circle, there are other latitudes for which traveling east or west for a half mile, a third of a mile, a fourth of a mile, or another such fraction of a mile would describe a complete circle. Either or both of the explorers could have started from any point one mile north of any of these circles, subject only to the conditions that they start one mile north of two different circles and do not start at the same longitude.

Unexplained Theft

The burglar, aware of an alarm that monitored the doors, had broken in by jimmying and crawling through a small window not wired into the system. After helping himself to ground-floor valuables, he heard movement upstairs and ran to escape the quickest way. The back door opened easily from the inside.

The Universal Solvent

In space. The so-called solvent is a black hole, which irreversibly absorbs everything that falls into it. Not all black holes are as massive as stars. The scientist has located a very small one and plans to guide it into orbit somehow, perhaps by feeding it suitable masses from precisely calculated positions.

Too Heavy

Since the machinery was made of sturdy metal with an awkward shape, the shipping clerk tried removing some superfluous cushioning material to make the package light enough. It didn't quite do the job, but he realized the resultant air spaces might accommodate helium-filled balloons. Adding these did sufficiently reduce the weight of the packed machinery—although only for a day or two until the helium leaked out.

Brian in Japan

Brian's slide show eventually showed a motor-vehicle factory where unfinished right-hand-drive cars (for use where people drive on the left side of the road) were coming off the line and identified the cars as being built for export to the USA. In the background, on a service road, a truck was being driven away from the factory on the right side of the road—and a car was driving toward it on the left side. The heckler in ferred correctly that the slide was backwards, because USA cars are left-hand drive. But because the slide was backwards, it proved that the Japanese drive on the left side of the road, which the heckler had not previously known. Brian never noticed that the slides, which showed two-way traffic, were backwards. He could not possibly have missed that fact had he been to Japan.

Unsolved Robbery

The two men are in prison. The second man robbed the bank and was not identified, but he was promptly arrested for another crime and given a long sentence for it.

Wrong Again!

The foreman had started counting with the ground floor as 1, up one flight as 2, and so on until reaching 15. He did not allow for the absence of a floor numbered thirteen, and he found painters on what was called the sixteenth floor.

You Have to Stop

The sign is on a chain across a private road, and the chain is padlocked between two posts to exclude trespassers. Because the chain is hard to see, a STOP sign suspended from it serves as a useful reminder to get out of the car and temporarily unfasten the chain.

Sprayed at the Lawn Again

The electrical power had been off for about an hour. In his house, Henry would have noticed that the clocks and other electronic devices that monitor the time (VCRs, for example) needed to be reset.

Safe Landing

The tree had been recently uprooted by a tornado, and it lay sideways on the ground. The top was only about ten feet from the ground, and Vic hung from it before jumping.

Spoken by the Book

The book was an unabridged dictionary.

Brian and the Ant

Brian was describing the preserved remains of a theoretically impossible creature. Ants, like all insects, receive oxygen not through lungs but through breathing tubes. These tubes circulate oxygen by diffusion, without the aid of a heart, a diaphragm, or any other pumping device. Diffusion works well only for small distances, so a large ant would suffocate. Also, if an ant doubles in every linear dimension, then the cross-section area of its legs increases to four times the original area. This, of course, increases the ant's leg strength fourfold. But every part of the ant increases in three dimensions. Each part of the ant, therefore the entire ant, increases its weight to eight times the original weight. Doubling the size of an ant, therefore, increases its weight twice as much as its strength. A sufficiently large ant, by using similar reasoning, would be too weak to stand and may even promptly collapse in on itself.

INDEX

Page key: puzzle, *clue*, **solution**